Medical Interpreters' Glossary

English-Arabic

Abe Lomri

DEDICATION

Glossary is your door to any profession. Build it, study it, ... and you are already there.

As I press ctrl +alt +space, I see three language preferences on my computer: English, French, and Arabic. Both English and French are Latin based, while Arabic has its own letters. English is written from left to right, while Arabic goes from right to left. I only have Latin letters on my keyboard because I have had to memorize the Arabic keyboard for a job.

On one side of the coin, we, as language professionals, somehow came to the realization that language barriers hinder access to life saving information and resources. So many of us took on an interventionist approach to language access. On the other side, the answer is simple when we measure the ROI in language services. At some point, everyone who is interested in selling or buying a product or service internationally will seek language services. With motivation, humans find a way to communicate, regardless of any perceived barriers.

I dedicate these glossaries to everyone and everything that motivated me to promote mutual understanding.

INTRODUCTION

Alphabetize

Building your medical glossary is as simple as putting new vocabulary in an excel sheet. Make sure you label your excel sheet, and let the software alphabetize for you! As interpreters our translation memory is our brains. Therefore, revisiting the glossary is a must.

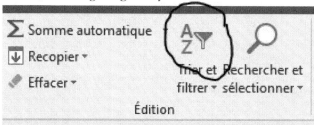

Word Search

Now that I have entered my words and phrases into an alphabetized excel sheet, how can I find terms when I need them?

The simple way to locate your terms is by alphabetically going down your list of terms. You can also do a word search. The word search option happens to conveniently neighbor the AZ filter to the right! You can search by entering the entire word in the search tab, or merely part of it:

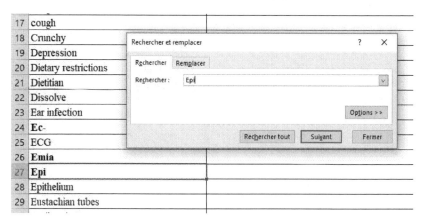

CONTENTS

DEDICATION   iii

اهداء

INTRODUCTION   iv

مقدمــة

1 **COVID-19:**   1

فيروس كورونا المستجد/كوفد-19

2 **Health Care Administration:**   Pg #4

إدارة الرعــاية الصحية

3 **Anatomy:**   Pg #12

التشريـــح

4 **Women's Health:**   Pg #16

الصحة النسائية

5 **Most Common Diseases & Immunizations:**   Pg #28

الأمراض والتطعيمـــات الأكثر شيــوعًا

6 **Medical Tests:**   Pg #30

فحــوصات طبية

7 **Conclusion:**   Pg #32

خـــاتمة

8 **About the Author**   Pg #35

عن المؤلف

CHAPTER 1

فيروس كورونا المستجد/كوفد-19   COVID-19

Asymptomatic	بدون أعراض ظاهرة
Authorization	ترخيص
CDC	مركز مكافحة الأمراض
Clinical infection	العدوى السريرية
clinical trials	التجارب السريرية
Cluster or outbreak clusters	مجموعات التفشي
Community mitigation strategies	استراتيجيات التخفيف المجتمعية
Coronavirus	فيروس كورونا المستجد
Covid-19	كوفيد-19
Curve	منحنى
Developed diagnostic test	اختبارات التشخيص المتقدمة
Droplet	قطيرة، قطرة صغيرة
Epidemic threshold	عتبة الوباء
ER	طوارئ، مستعجلات
Face mask	قناع الوجه
Flu	نزلة البرد، رشح
Hand sanitizer	معقم اليدين
Hand wash	غسل اليدين
Herd immunity	مناعة جماعية
Hydroxychloroquine	هيدروكسي كلوروكوين

ICU	وحدة العناية المركزة
Incubation	الاحتضان
Incubation period	فترة الحضانة
Infection	عدوى
Intravenous infusion	التسريب الوريدي
Layover	توقف مؤقت
MERS: Middle East respiratory syndrome	متلازمة الشرق الأوسط التنفسية
N95 Respirator mask	قناع التنفس N95
New variant	سلالة جديدة
Non-Pharmaceutical interventions (NPIs)	التدخلات غير الدوائية/ الصيدلانية
Novel	جديد
Outbreak	اندلاع، تفشي
Pandemic level	مستوى الوباء
Personal protective equipment (PPE)	معدات الحماية الشخصية (PPE)
Person-to-person	من شخص لآخر
Prevention	وقاية
Quarantine	الحجر صحي؛ عزلة الزامية؛ كرنتينا محجر صحي
Resilience	القدرة على الصمود، القدرة على التكيف
Respirator	جهاز تنفس
SARS: Severe acute respiratory syndrome	مرض الالتهاب الرئوي الحاد، فيروس
Screening	فحص
Self-isolation	العزلة الذاتية
Serology test	اختبار الأمصال
Severe	وخيم
Social distancing	إبعاد أو ابتعاد اجتماعي
Spread	انتقال، انتشار
State of emergency	حالة طوارئ
Stigma	وصمه عار
Swab test	اختبار المسحة

Symptomatic	مصحوب بأعراض
Symptoms	أعراض
Travel	سفر
Virus	فيروس
WHO	منظمة الصحة العالمية

CHAPTER 2

Health Care Administration	إدارة الرعاية الصحية
Abdominal discomfort	وجع البطن
Abscess	خراج
Acute pain	ألم حاد
Admissions	القبول
Admissions desk	مكتب القبول
Adrenaline	مادة الأدرينالين (ابينفرين)
Adverse reaction	ردة فعل معاكسة
Advice nurse	ممرضة للاستشارة
Allergen	مسببات الحساسية
Allergic reaction	ردة فعل تحسسية
Allergy	حساسية
Anesthesia	مخدر
Anesthesiologist	اخصائي التخدير
Anesthesiology	علم التخدير
Antibacterial	مضاد للجراثيم
Antibiotic	مضاد حيوي
Antibodies	مضادات الأجسام
Anticoagulant	مضاد للتجلط / التخثر
Antidote	مضاد للسم / ترياق
Anti-fungal	مضاد للفطريات
Antihistamine	مضاد الهيستامين

Anti-inflammatory	مضاد للالتهاب
Antiseptic	مطهر
Appendectomy	عملية استئصال الزائدة
Appendicitis	التهاب الزائدة
Asphyxia	اختناق
Aspirin	أسبرين
Asthma	ربو
Asthmatic	له علاقة بالربو / ربوي
Athlete's foot	سعفة القدم
Attending physician	الطبيب الحاضر
Bacteria	جراثيم
Bacterial infection	التهاب جرثومي
Bandage	ضماد
Band-aid	ضمادة صغيرة
Bee venom	س م النحل
Billing's method	طريقة تحضير الفواتير
Birthday	تاريخ الميلاد
Blister	تقرح جلدي
Blood	دم
Blood bank	بنك الدم
Blood clot	علقة / تخثر الدم
Blood pressure	ضغط الدم
Body ache	وجع الجسم
Bone splint	تجبير العظام
Breath	نفس
Breathe deeply	تنفس بعمق
Breathing problems	مشاكل بالتنفس
Bruise	كدمة / كدمات
Burning sensation	احساس بالحرقة
Cast	تجبيره العظم
Chest discomfort/tightness	توعك / ضيق بالصدر
Choke	اختناق
Chronic	مزمن
Circulatory	له علاقة بالدورة الدموية

Cold	برد / رشح
Colonoscopy	تنظير القولون (المعي الغليظ)
Compress	كمادة ضاغطة
Congested	محتقن
Consent	موافقة
Constipated	عنده امساك / آتم
Cotton balls/pads	كرات / كمادات قطنية
Cough	سعال / قحة
Cough medicine/ cough syrup/cough drop	دواء للسعال / شراب للسعال / قطرة للسعال
Coughing	يسعل / يقح
Crutch	عكاز
D&C (Dilatation & Curettage)	التوسيع والكشط (دي. آند سي.)
Decongestant	علاج للاحتقان
Diabetes	مرض السكري
Diagnose	تشخيص
Diagnosis	تشخيصات
Disable	معاق
Discomfort	توعك
Dislocated	مخلوع
Dizziness	مصاب بالدوار
Doctor's office	مكتب الطبيب
Dressing	تضميد
Drop	قطرة / نقطة
Drowsiness	مصاب بالنعاس
Drugstore	صيدلية
Dull pain	ألم كليل
Earache	ألم في الأذن
Ear lobe	شحمة الأذن
Ear tube	قناة الأذن
Ear wax	شمع الأذن
Emergency room (ER)	غرفة الطوارئ
Emphysema	انتفاخ رئوي
Endoscopy	تنظير داخلي

Enema	حقنة شرجية
Epidural	ابيدورال / ابرة مخدرة تعطى عادة للنساء أثناء الولادة
Eye drops	قطرات للعين
Family history	التاريخ الصحي للعائلة
Fasting	صائما / صائمة
Feces	البراز / الروث
Fever	حمى / حرارة
Fever blister	تقرح جلدي من الحرارة
Flu	رشح / برد
Food allergy	حساسية للطعام
Fractured	مكسور
Front desk	مكتب الاستعلامات في المدخل
Gauze	شاش
General practitioner	طبيب عام
Glucose tests	فحوص الغلوغوز / السكر
Gnawing pain	ألم قارض
Gown/ (hospital gown)	ثوب / (ثوب المستشفى)
Gynecologist	طبيب نسائي
Hacking cough	سعالا متقطعا جافا
hay fever	حمى القش / غبار الطلع
Headache	وجع رأس
Health	صحة
Heart attack	نوبة قلبية
Heart murmur	نفخات / حفيف القلب
Heavy lifting	حمل ثقيل
Height	الطول
Hernia	الفتق
High blood pressure	ضغط الدم المرتفع
Hives	شرى / نوع من الطفح الجلدي
Hoarse	أجش (للصوت)
Hospital gown	ثوب مستشفى
Household chemicals	مواد كيماوية منزلية
Hurt	ألم / اصابة / جرح

Hypersensitivity	حساسية مرتفعة
Immunoglobulin E (igE)	غلوبولين اي. للمناعة
Infection	عدوى / خمج / انتان
Inflammation	التهاب
Inhaler	أداة للاستنشاق
Inpatient	مريض داخلي
Insulin	انسولين
Intensive care unit	وحدة العناية المشددة
Irregular pulse	نبضات غير منتظمة
Itch	حكة
Itching	حكة
Joint	مفصل / وصلة
Laparoscopy	تنظير البطن
Laser surgery	جراحة بأشعة الليزر
Ligament	رباط بين مفاصل الجسم
Lower back pain	ألم أسفل الظهر
Lump	كتلة
Maternity ward	قسم الولادة / الأمومة
Medical excuse	عذر طبي
Medical history	التاريخ الطبي
Medicated compress	مادة ضاغطة طبية
Medication	دواء
Middle ear infection	التهاب الأذن الوسطى
Mold	فطر / عفن
Nasal spray	بخاخ للأنف
Nauseating pain	ألم يسبب الغثيان
Nostril	فتحة الأنف
Numbing pain	ألم تخديري / تنميلي
Nurse	ممرضة
Nursery	الحضانة
Nurses' station	مركز الممرضات
Operate, to	يجري العملية
Operating room (OR)	غرفة العمليات
Operation	عملية

Outpatient	مريض خارجي
Over-the-counter medication	دواء لا يحتاج الى وصفة طبية
Oxygen	أوكسجين
Pain	ألم / وجع
Pass out	اغماء/ فقدان الوعي
Penicillin	بنسلين
Physical exam	فحص طبي
Pills	حبوب
Plugged ear	أذن مسدودة
Pollen allergy	حساسية لغبار الطلع
Prescription	وصفة طبية
Pressure	ضغط
Private room	غرفة خاصة
Pulse	نبض
Radiology	أشعة
Rashe(s)	طفح جلدي
Recovery room	غرفة النقاهة
Redness	احمرار
Rest	راحة
Rheumatic fever	حمى روماتيزمية / رثويه
Scab	الجرب
Scar	ندبة
Scratch	خمشة / جرح بسيط
Scrub, to (surgically)	تنظيف الأيدي قبل الدخول الى العملية
Seizure	نوبة صرع
Sexually transmitted disease	أمراض جنسية معدية
Sharp pain	ألم حاد
Shiver	رجفة / قشعريرة
Shortness of breath	ضيق في التنفس
Sinus infection	التهاب الجيوب الأنفية
Sleepy	نعسان
Sling	وشاح تعليق (الذراع المكسورة - عادة)
Sore, cold	قرحة الشفة / البرد

9

Sprain	فكش / ملخ / التواء
Stethoscope	سماعة الطبيب
Stitches	قطبة / غرزة / خياطة طبية
Stomach flu	نزلة / رشح على المعدة
Strain	جهد / ارهاق
Strenuous activity	نشاط مجهد
Strep throat	التهاب الحلق العقدي
Stroke	سكتة دماغية
Stuffed-up	محشو / ممتلئ
Stutter	تأتأة
Surgeon	طبيب جراح
Surgery	جراحة
Surgical procedure	عملية جراحية
Suture	غرزة خياطة طبية
Sweat	تعرق
Symptoms	أعراض / ظواهر (المرض)
Syringe	محقنة / ابرة
Tablets	حبوب
Temperature	حرارة
Thyroid	الغدة الدرقية
Triage nurse	ممرضة الفرز
Tubal ligation	ربط الأنابيب للمرأة
Tube	أنبوب
Tuberculosis	مرض السل
Ulcer	قرحة
Undergo surgery, to	يجري العملية
Urinalysis	تحليل البول
Urinary bladder	المبولة
Urinary problem	مشكلة بولية
Urinary tract	المجاري البولية
Urinating	التبول
Urine	بول
urine test	فحص بول
vital signs	الظواهر الحياتية

Vitamins	فيتامينات
Waiting room	غرفة الانتظار
Watery eyes	عيون دامعة
Weight	وزن
Wheezing	أزيز تنفسي
x-ray unit	وحدة الأشعة السينية

CHAPTER 3

Anatomy	التشريح
Abdomen	البطن
Adam's apple	جوزة الحلق
Adrenal glands	غدد الكظر (على الكليتين)
Amniotic fluid	السائل داخل المشيمة / الأمنيون
Ankle	الكاحل
Anus	الشرج
Appendix	الزائدة
Armpit	تحت الابط
Arms	الأذرع
Artery	الشريان
Back	الظهر
Backbone	العمود الفقري
Belly button	السرة
Big toe	أصبع الرجل الكبير
Bile	العصارة
Bladder	المبولة
Blood	الدم
Blood clot	علقة / تخثر الدم
Bodily fluids	سائل الجسم
Bone marrow	مخ العظام / النقي
Bowel movement	حركة الأمعاء / البراز

Brain	المخ / الدماغ
Brain stem	ساق الدماغ
Breast	الثدي
Buttock	الدبر
Calf	بطن الساق
Canal	قناة
Cartilage	غضروف
Cheek	الخد
Cheekbone	عظمة الخد
Chest	الصدر
Chin	الذقن
Collar bone	عظمة الترقوة
Colon	القولون / المعي المستقيم
Diaphragm	الحجاب الحاجز
Dimple	غمازة
Duct	قناة
Ear	الأذن
Elbow	الكوع
Esophagus	المري
Eye	العين
Eyeball	مقلة العين
Eyebrow	الحاجب
Eyelashes	الأهداب رموش العيون
Eye lid	جفن العين
Eye socket	بؤرة العين
Femur	عظم الفخذ
Finger	الاصبع
Fingertip	رأس الاصبع / أنامل
Forearm	الذراع
Forehead	جبهة الرأس
Gall bladder	المرارة
Genitals	الأعضاء التناسلية
Groin	المغابن
Hair	الشعر

Hands	اليدين
Heart	القلب
Heel	الكعب
Hip	الورك
Index finger	أصبع السبابة
Jaw	الفك
Joint	المفصل
Kidney	الكلية
Knee	الركبة
Knuckle	المفاصل أو العظام الصغيرة في اليد أو الرجل
Large intestine	الأمعاء الغليظة
Larynx	الحنجرة
Legs	الأرجل
Limb	الطرف
Lips	الشفاه
Liver	الكبد
Lungs	الرئتان
Lymph gland	غدة لمفاوية
Lymph node	عقدة لمفاوية
Mammary glands	الغدد الثدية
Middle finger	الاصبع الأوسط
Mouth	الفم
Muscle	العضلة
Nails	الأظافر
Nape	مؤخرة الرقبة
Neck	الرقبة
Nipple	حلمة الثدي
Ovaries	المبايض
Palm	راحة اليد
Pancreas	البانكرياس
Phlegm	البلغم
Plasma	بلازما (الدم)
Rectum	الشرج

Rib	الضلع
Ribcage	القفص الصدري
Saliva	اللعاب
Scalp	فروة الرأس
Scapula	عظم الكتف
Shin	الذقن
Shoulder	الكتف
Shoulder blade	لوح الكتف
Skull	الجمجمة
Small intestine	الأمعاء الدقيقة
Spinal column	العمود الفقري
Spine	العمود الفقري
Spleen	طحال
Sputum	مبصقة
Stomach	المعدة
Stomach lining	غشاء المعدة
Teeth	الأسنان
Temple	الصدغ
Thorax	الجزء الأعلى من الصدر
Throat	الحلق
Thumb	الابهام
Thyroid gland	الغدة الدرقية
Toes	أصابع القدم
Tonsils	اللوز
Trachea	الرغامي / القصبة الهوائية
Tract	مجرى
Uterine lining	غشاء الرحم
Uterus	الرحم
Vein	الوريد
Waist	الخصر
Windpipe	القصبة الهوائية / الرغامي
Womb	الرحم
Wrist	الرسغ

CHAPTER 4

Women's Health	الصحة النسائية
Abdominal delivery	ولادة من البطن
Abdominal pregnancy	حمل في البطن
Abortion	اجهاض
Afterbirth	بعد الولادة
Amniocentesis	سحب عينة من سائل المشيمة لفحصها
Amniotic fluid	سائل المشيمة
Anguish	ألم نفسي / آرب
At term birth	ولادة مكتملة فترة الحمل
Bear down, to	ادفعي للأسفل
Bed pan	نونية السرير
Bed rest	راحة في السرير
Birth	ولادة

Birth canal	قناة الولادة
Birth control	تحديد النسل
Birth injury	اصابة / جراح الولادة
Bleeding	نزيف
Bloated	منفوخة البطن / متخومة
Block	انحصار / انسداد
Bodily changes	تغيرات جسدية
Bottle-feed	الرضاع من القارورة (صناعيا)
Bowel movement, stools	حركة الأمعاء/ البراز
Breast-care	العناية بالثدي
Breastfeed	الرضاع من الثدي
Breast mass	كتلة في الثدي
Breast milk	حليب الثدي
Breast pump	مضخة الثدي
Breast self-examination	فحص ذاتي للثدي
Breast tenderness	ألم في الثدي عند اللمس
Breech delivery	ولادة ومقعد الطفل لأسفل
Burning sensation	احساس بالحرقة
C-section/Caesarian section	ولادة قيصرية
Cervical pregnancy	حمل في عنق الرحم
Cesarean delivery	ولادة قيصرية

Cervix	عنق الرحم
Charley horse	ألم عضلي
Chills	بردية
Cold	برد / رشح
Colic	مغص في البطن
Colostrum	لباء/صمغة/ سائل ما قبل حليب الرضاع
Complicated labor	ولادة معقدة
Condom	عازل مطاطي للذكر
Congested, to be	يكون محتقنا
Cracked nipples	حلمة ثدي مشققة
Cradle	سرير
Cradle, to	يضع في السرير
Cramps, stomach	معص / تشنج عضلات المعدة
Crankiness	متعكر المزاج
Crib	سرير الطفل
D&C dilation and curettage	التوسيع والكشط (دي. آند سي.)
Dead birth	ولادة جنين ميت
Deliver	تولد
Delivery	ولادة
Delivery room	غرفة الولادة
Delivery table	طاولة الولادة

"Dermoplast" spray	بخاخ ترقيع الجلد
Depo-Provera shot	حقنة/ابرة منع الحمل دييو- بروفيرا
Diaper rash	طفح جلدي من الحفاض
Diaphragm	الحجاب الحاجز
Diarrhea	اسهال
Discharge instructions	تعليمات الخروج من المستشفى
Dizziness	مصاب بالدوار
Douche	دوش / نضح / نج
Drainage	تصريف
Dry labor	ولادة جافة
Dryness	جفاف
Due date	تاريخ الولادة (المتوقع)
Dysmenorrhea	عسر الحيض
Earache	ألم أذن
Ear infection	التهاب أذن
Dysuria	عسر (حصر) بول
Ectopic pregnancy	حمل خارج الرحم
Egg	بويضة / بيضة
Endometriosis	ورم بطانة الرحم
Endometrium	ورم في بطانة الرحم
Engorged, to be	يكون محتقن

Episiotomy	عملية (شق) في الفرج
Epidural anesthesia	مخدر ايبيدورال (ابرة في الظهر)
Estrogen replacement treatment	معالجة استبدال الاستروجين
Express out the milk, to	عصر الحليب خارجا
Fallopian tube	أنبوب / قناة فالوب
False labor	طلق ولادة وهمي / كاذب
Family planning	تحديد النسل
Female sterility	عقم الأنثى
Fertility counseling	استشارة في العقم
Fertilization treatment	معالجة بالتخصيب
Fibroid	ليفة
Fibrous tumor	ورم ليفي
Flu	رشح / برد
Forceps delivery	ولادة بملقط / شفاطة التوليد
Foul smell of vaginal discharge	رائحة كريهة من سيلان مهبلي
Frigidity	فتور جنسي
FSH follicle stimulating hormone	هرمون حث الجريبات
Genetic counseling	استشارة عن عوامل الوراثة
Genetic trend	الاتجاه الوراثي
Genitalia	الأعضاء التناسلية
Gestational diabetes	مرض سكري بالحمل

Grip	النزلة الوافدة / انفلونزا (جريب)
Give birth, to	تولد
Growth and development	النمو والتطور
Hemorrhage	نزيف
Hemorrhoids	بواسير
Hind milk, to	لَبَنُ آخِرِ الرَّضْعَة
Hormonal treatment	معالجة بالهرمونات
Hot and cold spells	نوبة حرارة ونوبة بردية
Hot flashes	نوبات حارة (بعد سن اليأس)
Hysterectomy	استئصال الرحم
Ibuprofen	مسكن آلام ايبوبرفين
Ice pack	كيس ثلج
Induced labor	تحريض الولادة
Increased pain of episiotomy	زيادة ألم شق الفرج
Induced abortion	تحريض الاجهاض
Infertile	عقيم
Inhalers, puffers	أدوات استنشاق (شهيق) وزفير / بخاخات
Intrauterine device (IUD)	مانع حمل بالرحم (آي.يو.دي.)
In-vitro fertilization	تخصيب في الانبوب
Itchiness	حكة
Labia	الشفة / الشفر

Labor	المخاض / الولادة
Labor pains	آلام الولادة
Labor room	غرفة الولادة
Labor, to be in	تكون في مرحلة الولادة / الوضع
Lactation	در الحليب / الارضاع
Lamaze method	طريقة لاماز
Latched on (to breast)	ملتقط / قابض على (الثدي)
Lethargic	النعاس / مرض النعاس العقلي
Lice	القمل
Lip of the pudendum	شفة / شفر الفرج
Listlessness	فتور الهمة / البلادة
Live birth	ولادة المولود حيا
LOP Length of pregnancy	طول فترة الحمل
Lukewarm	فاتر
Mammogram, mammography,	تصوير الثدي بالأشعة (ماموغرام)
Menopause	انقطاع الحيض /سن اليأس
Menstruation period, period	فترة الحيض / الدورة الشهرية
Midwife	قابلة التوليد
Milk pump	مضخة حليب
Miscarriage	اجهاض
Mood swings	تقلب المزاج

Morning-after pill	حبة الصباح التالي
Morning sickness	الوحام
Multiple birth	ولادة متعددة الأجنة
Multiple pregnancy	حمل متعدد الأجنة
Mucus	مخاط
Narrow hips	أوراك ضيقة
Nebulizer	بخاخة
Nipple discharge	سيلان من الحلمة
Night sweats	تعرق أثناء النوم
Norplant (contraceptive implant)	نوربلانت (كبسولات تزرع لمنع الحمل)
Nursing pads	كمادات الرضاعة
Oral contraceptive	موانع الحمل عن طريق الفم
Overactive bladder	مبولة نشطة أكثر من اللزوم
Ovary	المبيض
Ovarian pregnancy	حمل في المبايض
Oviduct	قناة مبيضية
Painkiller	مسكن للآلام
PMS-Pre-Menstrual Syndrome	(بي. أم. اس.) ظاهرة ما قبل الدورة الشهرية
Pap smear	باب سمير / فحص نسائي سرطاني للمجاري التناسلية
Parturient	بحالة المخاض / الولادة

Pass a clot, to	تمرير العلقة في الدم
Patch	لصقة
Postpartum depression (baby blues)	اكتئاب بعد الولادة
Permanent sterility	عقم دائم
Post-term birth	ولادة بعد اكتمال فترة الحمل
Precipitate labor	ولادة عاجلة
Pregnancy	حمل
Pregnant	حامل
Premature	قبل أوانه
Premature birth	ولادة قبل الأوان
Premature labor, delivery	ولادة قبل أوانها
Prenatal	قبل الولادة / أثناء الحمل
Prolonged labor	مخاض طويل
Pump out the milk, to	ضخ الحليب خارجا
Rash	طفح جلدي
Runny nose	سيلان الأنف / برد
Sanitary napkins/pads	محارم معقمة/كمادات التنظيف
Scraping	تنظيف قبل العملية / الولادة
Sitz-baths	حمام قعود
Sore nipples	حلمات متقرحة
Sore throat	التهاب الحلق

Spontaneous labor	ولادة تلقائية
Sperm	النطفة / المني
Spitting up	البصاق
Spontaneous abortion	اجهاض تلقائي
Spotting	رؤية بقع / نقط
Staples	غرز / خياطة طبية
Sterility	عقم / تعقيم
Steri-strips	شرائط تعقيم
Still-birth	ولادة جنين ميت
Still-born	ولد الجنين ميت
Stitches	قطبة / غرزة خياطة (الجرح)
Stool problem	مشكلة بالبراز
Stool softener	ملين البراز
Stuffed, to be	محشو / متخم
Symptoms	أعراض / ظواهر
Tampons	تامبون / كمادة نسائية
Tiredness	تعب
Threaten abortion	تهديد بالإجهاض
Therapeutic abortion	اجهاض علاجي
Trained midwife	قابلة توليد مدربة
Tubal pregnancy	حمل في الأنبوب

Tummy	البطن
Twin pregnancy	حمل توأم
Ultrasound	موجات فوق الصوتية (ألتراساوند)
Umbilical cord	حبل السرة
Untrained midwife	قابلة توليد غير مدربة
Uterine cramps, after-pains	مغص في الرحم / الآلام اللاحقة
Uterine tenderness	تألم باللمس
Vaginal bleeding	نزيف المهبل
Vaginal cream	كريم (مرهم) للمهبل
Vaginal discharge	خروج سائل من المهبل
Vaginal dryness	جفاف في المهبل
Vaginal jelly	مادة هلامية (جيلي) للمهبل
Vaginal lubricant	ملين / تزييت المهبل
Vaginal yeast infection	التهاب فطري في المهبل
Varicose veins	أوردة الدوالي
Water soluble lubricant	مادة تزييت تنحل بالماء
Watery discharge	خروج الماء
Wean, to	تفطم
Wheezing	أزيز تنفسي
Witch hazel	شجرة يستعمل عودها وورقها كمادة مقلصة للأنسجة

	شجرة الويتشهازل
1st. stage of labor	المرحلة الأولى للولادة
2d. stage of labor	المرحلة الثانية للولادة
3d. stage of labor	المرحلة الثالثة للولادة

CHAPTER 5

Most Common Diseases & Immunizations	الأمراض والتطعيمات الأكثر شيوعًا

Asthma	الربو
Additional shots	ابر / حقن اضافية
Booster shots	ابر / حقن منشطة
Bronchitis	التهاب القصبات
By mouth	عن طريق الفم
Chicken pox (Varicella)	جدري الماء
Diphtheria-Tetanus-Pertussis (DTP) Three-in-one shot/baby shot	دفتريا (خانوق) – تيتانوس (الكزاز) – برتوسيس(السعال الديكي/ الشهاقة) د بت ب. ثلاثة في حقنة واحدة / ابرة الطفل
Drops	قطرات / نقاط
Flu	برد / رشح
German measles	حصبة ألمانية
Give a shot, to	يعطي ابرة / حقنة
Hay fever	حمى القش / غبار الطلع
Hepatitis B	التهاب الكبد الوبائي ب
Haemophilus, Influenza, Meningitis (HIB vaccine)	تلقيح / تطعيم نزف الدم/ انفلونزا / التهاب السحايا (تلقيح هـ. آي. ب.)
Immunization	التلقيح / التطعيم
Immunization chart	لائحة التلقيح

Immunization-booster dose	جرعة منشطة للتلقيح
Immunize, to	يلقح / يطعم
Jaundice	الصفيراء
Malaria	الملاريا
Measles	الحصبة
Meningitis	التهاب السحايا
Mumps	النكاف
Pneumonia	التهاب الرئة
Polio	شلل الأطفال
Rabies	الكلب
Rubella	الحصبة الألمانية / الحميراء
Shot	ابرة / حقنة
Shot chart/ shot record	لائحة التلقيح / سجل التلقيح
Scarlet fever	الحمى القرمزية
Smallpox	الجدري
Syringe	ابرة / حقنة
Tetanus	الكزاز
Tonsillitis	التهاب اللوز
Tuberculosis (BCG)	السل (بي.سي.جي)
Typhoid	التيفوئيد
Typhoid fever	حمى التيفوئيد
Vaccinate, to	يلقح
Vaccination	تلقيح
Whooping cough	السعلة الشهاقة / السعال الديكي
Yellow fever	الحمى الصفراء

CHAPTER 6

MEDICAL TESTS	فحوصات طبية

Blood test, blood work	فحص دم
Blood smear	مسحة دم
CBC complete blood count0	تعداد كامل لكريات الدم
CAT scan (computerized axial tomography)	مسح طبقي محوري (كات سكان)
CT scan (computed tomography)	مسح طبقي (سي.تي. سكان)
Eye exam	فحص العيون
ECG Electrocardiogram	تخطيط القلب كهربائيا (اي.سي.جي)
EEG electroencephalogram	تخطيط الدماغ كهربائيا
ELISA test	فحص انزيمات نقص المناعة (اليزا تيست)
Fasting blood sugar	فحص صائم للسكر في الدم
Glucose tolerance test	فحص تحمل الغلوكوز
Hearing test	فحص السمع
MRI Magnetic Resonance Imaging	فحص التصوير بالمرنان المغناطيسي (م.ر.آي.)
Pelvic examination	فحص الحوض
Physical Therapy (PT)	علاج طبيعي
Post-operative tests	فحوصات بعد العملية
Pre-operative tests	فحوصات قبل العملية

Pulmonary function test	فحص وظيفة الرئة
Rectal examination	فحص الشرج
RBC red blood count	عد الكريات الحمر
Skin test	فحص الجلد
Sonogram	فحص بالموجات الصوتية (سونوغرام)
Stool specimen	عينة براز
(SGOT) serum glutamic oxaloacetic transaminase	مصل الغلوتاميك (اس.جي.أو.تي)
Stress test	فحص ضغط الجهد على القلب
SR sedimentation rate	معدل الترسبات (اس.آر.)
Urine routine, urinalysis	تحليل البول
WBC white blood count	عد الكريات البيضاء

CONCLUSION

Trainers and instructors are welcome to build guided role-play scenarios using this medical glossary. In fact, I have written an *Interpretation Role-Play* book that uses the same method. Here is a sample activity from the book:

Exercise 1: Tuberculosis

Glossary in Context:

Source	Target
Active tuberculosis	
Congested	
Cough	
Immune system	
Cough	
Pain relieve medicine	
TB skin test	
Chest x-ray	
Medical condition	
Weight loss	

Script: Please note that only source language is provided. The activity requires that you come up with the target language response. The activity necessitates at least three individuals for interpreting to be possible. At the end of the session, you can grade each other. Both interpreter and patient are quizzed because the activity is intended for training at least two interpreters at a time. The person playing the patient's role will have to provide their statement based on the interpreters' rendition. You are also welcome to substitute OZ, Kansas and Smith with your names to make the exercise more fun! The arrows on the left side at the beginning of the activity are to demonstrate where interpreters proceed with interpreting.

D: Mr. Smith, I understand you are new to the country. Welcome to OZ!

I: --

P: ---

I: Thank you!

D: What is the reason for your visit today?

I: --

P: --

I: I have been having a severe **cough**, which I am thinking is due to change in the weather, but I cannot sleep well because I get **congested**.

D: How long have you had this cough?

I: ---

P: ---

I: I would say three to four weeks.

D: Any blood with the cough?

I: ---

P: ---

I: Well, I started coughing as I was brushing my teeth yesterday, and I noticed there was some blood in my mouth. I don't know if it was from the teeth or the cough.

D: Have you experienced in sudden or unexplained **weight loss** recently?

I: ---

P: ---

I: I went from **90 to 75 kilograms** in the last three weeks, but I have not been eating much since I arrived at OZ. The food here is surely different from the food in Kansas.

D: That's right, the food in Kansas is much better. Have you had contact with anyone with **active tuberculosis** disease in the past year?

I: --?

P: ---

I: Not that I know of.

D: Do you have a **medical condition**, or are you taking medications, which suppress your **immune system**?

I: --?

P: ---

I: No, I am only taking **pain relieve medicine**.

D: I cannot give you anything for the cough until we run some tests. The nurse will come to draw your blood and give you a **TB skin test**. He will also give you an appointment to get a **chest x-ray.**

Rubric:

This is a simplified rubric for your activity. Consider issues of accuracy, not only in grammar and vocabulary, but also in register, names and numbers, as well any addition or omission. Name the error type if any while providing feedback.

Correct (+)	
Incorrect (-)	
Total-- /20	

Feedback:

There are two types of tuberculosis: dormant and active TB. Doctors ask questions to assess if a person might have TB. They also order tests to be sure. After diagnosis is made, patients follow a course of treatment, depending on the type of TB. Interpreters must be familiar with medical terminology and healthcare information for their interpreting to be accurate.

ABOUT THE AUTHOR

Abe Lomri is a Colorado State University Graduate, Fulbright Scholar, linguist, and the co-founder of Azur Linguist LLC. Author of *Interpretation Role-Play*, he trained interpreters physically in the US, France, Greece, Morocco, and West Africa. Virtually, he enjoyed training interpreters from all over the world.

Made in the USA
Monee, IL
29 September 2024

66876660R00024